Flute Technique

Overtones™

A Comprehensive Flute Series

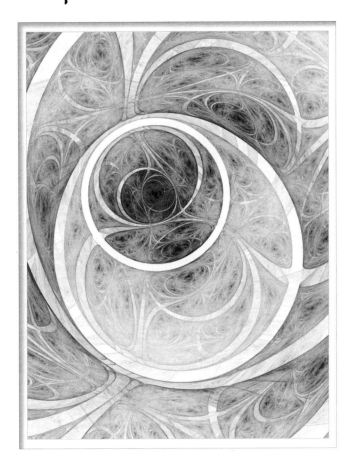

The Royal Conservatory™
The finest instrument is the mind.

FREDERICK HARRIS MUSIC

Overtones™: A Comprehensive Flute Series

It is with great enthusiasm that The Royal Conservatory presents this inaugural edition of *Overtones™: A Comprehensive Flute Series*. It is hoped that this groundbreaking new series will address the need for a single collection of quality educational materials to foster musical development and instill appreciation of the richness and diversity of music written for flute. The series is built on the premise of nurturing well-rounded musicianship, giving teachers and students everything they would expect in a comprehensive pedagogical resource along with a chance to explore their potential, push their boundaries, and broaden their horizons. Each piece has been carefully selected to ensure an expansive representation of musical styles from all eras. Students will encounter standard repertoire from well-known composers as well as exciting contemporary works from North America and around the world.

Overtones™ embraces a progressively leveled, multi-faceted approach, systematically organizing material into separate components: *Repertoire, Studies, Recordings, Orchestral Excerpts,* and *Technique*.

Flute Technique has been designed to assist students in building a technical foundation gradually and logically from the very first level of study (Preparatory) through to the advanced stages of musical development (Level 10). The technical exercises are selected and organized to complement the repertoire, studies, and orchestral excerpts that students are learning at the same level, and to prepare adequately for the challenges of the next level. By studying the material for their level over the course of the year, students should find that they are well prepared to meet these challenges.

The study of all technical exercises in this book should be cumulative; the selection of keys, articulations, and minimum tempo requirements at each level were determined with examination purposes in mind. To facilitate examination preparation, a chart of articulation patterns for all levels and an overview chart for each level have been included so that students and teachers can see at a glance what is required and plan their course of study accordingly.

Flute Technique embraces a progressive approach: the keys listed for each level become increasingly difficult, the pitch range gradually expands, and the octave span extends from one to two and finally three octaves. In Levels Preparatory–6, the presentation of keys is by major and relative minor keys according to the circle of 5ths; in Levels 7–10, it is chromatic by major and tonic minor keys. All three forms of the minor scale are introduced at the lower levels to accomodate different approaches to teaching.

To avoid repeating technical excercises several times, not all exercises for each level are included. For Levels 7–10, if an exercise in a particular key has been introduced in the previous grade, it is not printed again; rather, students are instructed to refer to the previous page or in the case of chromatic scales, and diminished 7th arpeggios, to follow the pattern established in a provided example.

Helpful Hints

1. Technique is the foundation of musical language; it is important to spend time on technique every day.

2. Good technique requires playing smoothly and evenly, not merely playing faster. It results from developing a steady airflow, control, good intonation, even finger action, clear tonguing and articulation, and striking a balance between all these different elements.

3. Engage in active learning by memorizing the patterns for each technical exercise. Playing technique should be a tactile rather than a visual experience.

4. When practicing, be creative: experiment with playing the exercises in different rhythms and patterns.

For examination requirements of RCM Examinations and the National Music Certificate Program, please refer to the *Flute Syllabus, 2010 Edition*.

Contents

Articulation Patterns   4

Preparatory Level   5

Level 1   6

Level 2   8

Level 3   11

Level 4   14

Level 5   17

Level 6   21

Level 7   24

Level 8   34

Level 9   37

Level 10   42

Articulation Patterns

Articulation		Prep–Level 1	Level 2	Level 3	Level 4	Levels 5–6	Levels 7–8	Levels 9–10
all slurred	(long slur over 9 notes)	x	x	x	x	x	x	x
	(slur over 6 notes)	x		x	x	x	x	
all tongued	(9 tongued notes)	x	x	x	x	x	x	x
	(6 tongued notes)	x		x	x	x	x	
two slurred, two tongued				x	x	x	x	x
two slurred, one tongued				x	x	x	x	
two tongued, two slurred					x	x	x	x
one tongued, two slurred					x	x	x	
two slurred, two slurred						x	x	x
three slurred, one tongued							x	x
one tongued, three slurred							x	x
one tongued, two slurred, one tongued								x

Prepara

Overview

Scales	Keys			Articulations
Major	C, G, F			
Minor	A, E, D			
Arpeggios				
Major	C, G, F			
Minor	A, E, D			

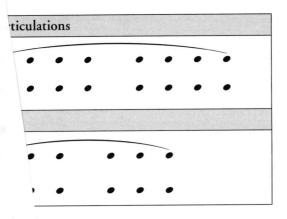

Scales ♩ = 60

C Major

G Major

F Major

D Minor

Arpeggios ♩ = 60

C Major

A Minor

G Major

E Minor

F Major

D Minor

Level 1

Overview

Scales	Keys	Range	Tempo	Note Values	Articulations
Major	C, G, F				
Minor (choice of natural, harmonic, or melodic)	A, E, D	1 octave	♩ = 60	♩	
Arpeggios					
Major	C, G, F				
Minor	A, E, D	1 octave	♩ = 60	♩	

Scales ♩ = 60

C Major

A Minor Natural

A Minor Harmonic

A Minor Melodic

G Major

E Minor Natural

E Minor Harmonic

E Minor Melodic

F Major

D Minor Natural

D Minor Harmonic

D Minor Melodic

Arpeggios ♩ = 60

C Major

A Minor

G Major

E Minor

F Major

D Minor

Level 2

Overview

Scales	Keys	Range	Tempo	Note Values	Articulations
Major	B♭	1 octave			
	C, G, D, F	2 octaves			
Minor (choice of natural, harmonic, or melodic)	A, B	1 octave	♩ = 60		
	E, D, G	2 octaves			
Chromatic	Beginning on D	1 octave			
Arpeggios					
Major	B♭	1 octave			
	C, G, D, F	2 octaves	♩ = 60		
Minor	A, B	1 octave			
	E, D, G	2 octaves			

Scales ♩ = 60

C Major

A Minor Natural (1 octave)   A Minor Harmonic (1 octave)

A Minor Melodic (1 octave)

G Major

E Minor Natural

E Minor Harmonic

E Minor Melodic

D Major

B Minor Natural (1 octave)

B Minor Harmonic (1 octave)

B Minor Melodic (1 octave)

F Major

D Minor Natural

D Minor Harmonic

D Minor Melodic

B♭ Major (1 octave)

G Minor Natural

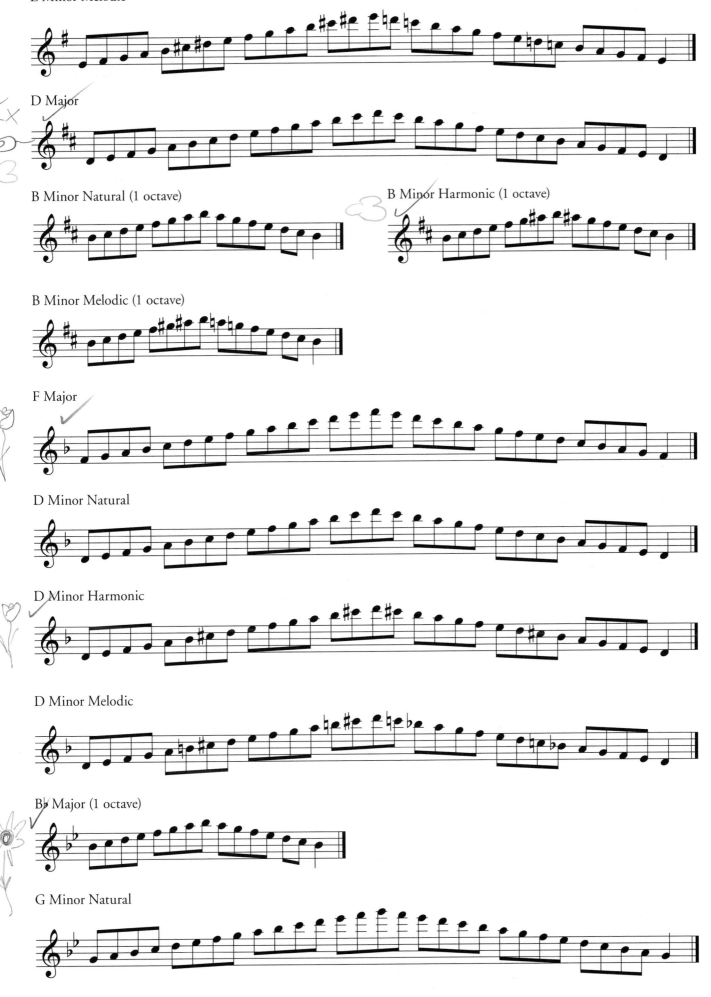

G Minor Harmonic

G Minor Melodic

Chromatic Scale ♩ = 60

Beginning on D (1 octave)

Arpeggios ♩ = 60

C Major

A Minor (1 octave)

G Major

E Minor

D Major

B Minor (1 octave)

F Major

D Minor

B♭ Major (1 octave)

G Minor

Level 3

Overview

Scales	Keys	Range	Tempo	Note Values	Articulations
Major	A, B♭	1 octave	♩ = 60	♫	
	G, D, E♭	2 octaves			
Minor (choice of harmonic or melodic)	B	1 octave			
	E, F♯, G, C	2 octaves			
Chromatic	Beginning on D	2 octaves			
Arpeggios					
Major	A, B♭	1 octave	♩ = 52	♪♪♪ 3	
	G, D, E♭	2 octaves			
Minor	B	1 octave			
	E, F♯, G, C	2 octaves			

Scales ♩ = 60

G Major

E Minor Harmonic

E Minor Melodic

D Major

B Minor Harmonic (1 octave)

B Minor Melodic (1 octave)

A Major (1 octave)

F# Minor Harmonic

F# Minor Melodic

Bb Major (1 octave)

G Minor Harmonic

G Minor Melodic

Eb Major

C Minor Harmonic

C Minor Melodic

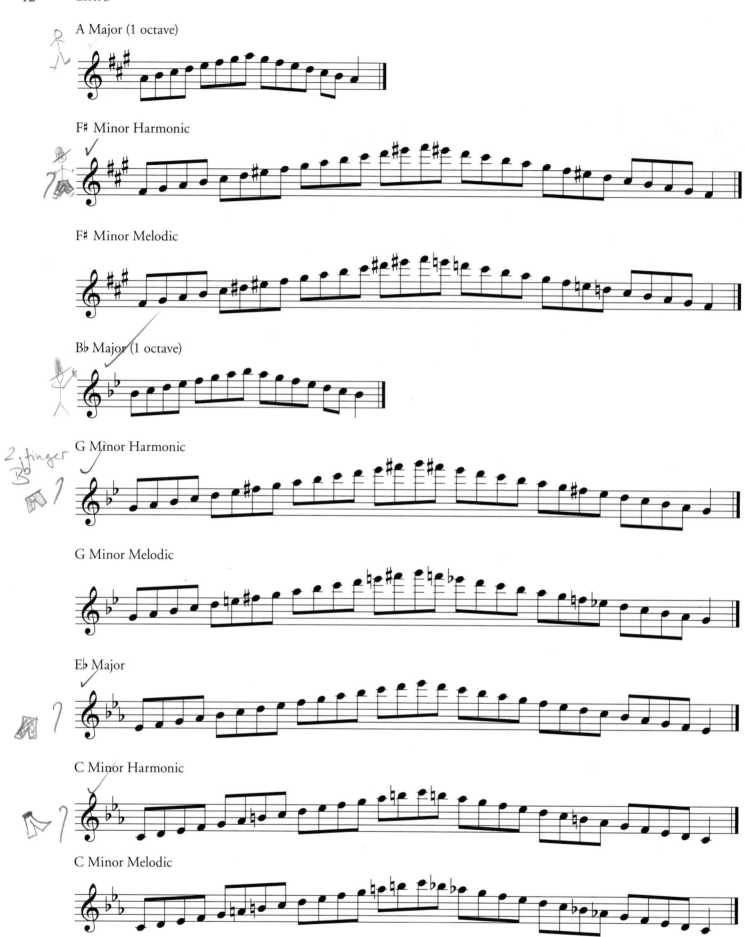

Chromatic Scale ♩ = 60

Beginning on D

Arpeggios ♩ = 52

Level 4

Overview

Scales	Keys	Range	Tempo	Note Values	Articulations
Major	A, E, E♭, A♭				See p. 4 for required articulations. Additional articulation for this level:
Minor (choice of harmonic or melodic)	F#, C#, C, F	2 octaves	♩ = 72		
Chromatic	Beginning on D				
Pentatonic (Major)	Beginning on D				
Arpeggios					
Major	A, E , E♭, A♭	2 octaves	♩ = 52		See p. 4 for required articulations. Additional articulation for this level:
Minor	F#, C#, C, F				
Dominant 7th of Major Keys	G	2 octaves	♩ = 72		

Scales ♩ = 72

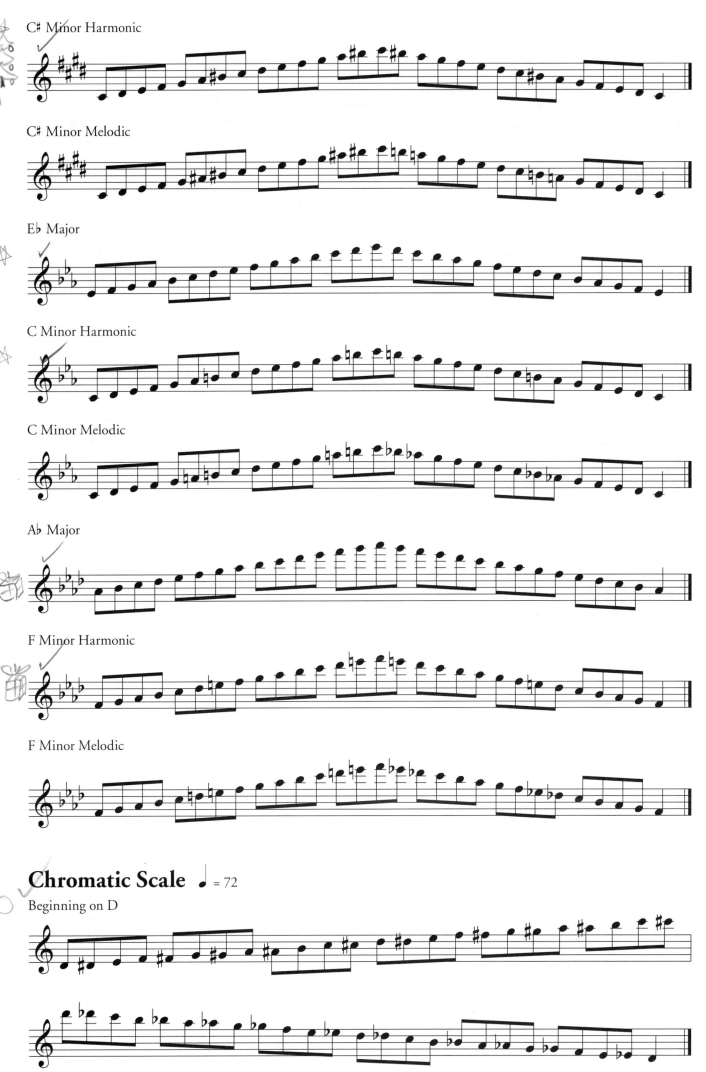

C♯ Minor Harmonic

C♯ Minor Melodic

E♭ Major

C Minor Harmonic

C Minor Melodic

A♭ Major

F Minor Harmonic

F Minor Melodic

Chromatic Scale ♩ = 72

Beginning on D

Pentatonic (Major) Scale ♩ = 72

Beginning on D

Arpeggios ♩ = 52

A Major

E Major

E♭ Major

A♭ Major

F♯ Minor

C♯ Minor

C Minor

F Minor

Dominant 7th Arpeggio ♩ = 72

G Major

Level 5

Overview

Scales	Keys	Range	Tempo	Note Values	Articulations
Major	B	1 octave	♩ = 80	♫	See p. 4 for required articulations. Additional articulation for this level: 
	E, B♭, A♭, D♭	2 octaves			
Minor (choice of harmonic or melodic)	A, C♯, G♯, F, B♭	2 octaves			
Chromatic	Beginning on C				
Pentatonic (Major)	Beginning on C				
Arpeggios					
Major	B	1 octave	♩ = 60	♪♪♪ (3)	See p. 4 for required articulations.
	E, B♭, A♭, D♭	2 octaves			
Minor	A, C♯, G♯, F, B♭	2 octaves			
Dominant 7th of Major Keys	C, G	2 octaves	♩ = 80	♫	See p. 4 for required articulations. Additional articulation for this level:

Scales ♩ = 80

A Minor Harmonic

A Minor Melodic

E Major

C♯ Minor Harmonic

C♯ Minor Melodic

B Major (1 octave)

G# Minor Harmonic

G# Minor Melodic

Bb Major

Ab Major

F Minor Harmonic

F Minor Melodic

Db Major (enharmonic equivalent of C# Major)

Bb Minor Harmonic

Bb Minor Melodic

Chromatic Scale ♩ = 80

Beginning on C

Pentatonic (Major) Scale ♩ = 80

Beginning on C

Arpeggios ♩ = 60

A Minor

E Major

C# Minor

B Major (1 octave)

G# Minor

Bb Major

Ab Major

F Minor

Db (enharmonic equivalent of C# Major)

Bb Minor

Dominant 7th Arpeggios ♩ = 80

C Major

G Major

Level 6

Overview

Scales	Keys	Range	Tempo	Note Values	Articulations
Major	B*, F♯, D♭				See p. 4 for required articulations.
Minor (choice of harmonic or melodic)	G♯, D♯, B♭				
Major in 3rds	C, G, F	2 octaves	♩ = 80	♫	
Chromatic	Beginning on G				
Pentatonic (Major)	Beginning on G				
Arpeggios					
Major	B*, F♯, D♭	2 octaves	♩ = 60	♪♪♪ (3)	See p. 4 for required articulations.
Minor	G♯, D♯, B♭				
Dominant 7th of Major Keys	F, B♭	2 octaves	♩ = 80	♫	See p. 4 for required articulations.

* Two-octave exercises beginning on B must be played up to B3.

Scales  = 80

B Major

G♯ Minor Harmonic

G♯ Minor Melodic

F♯ Major (enhramonic equivalent of G♭ Major)

D♯ Minor Harmonic (enharmonic equivalent of E♭ Minor)

D♯ Minor Melodic (enharmonic equivalent of E♭ Minor)

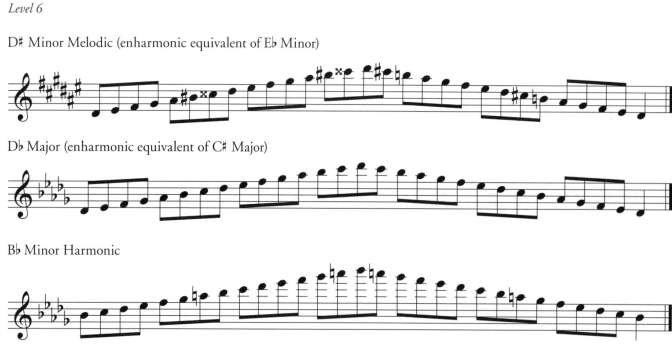

D♭ Major (enharmonic equivalent of C♯ Major)

B♭ Minor Harmonic

B♭ Minor Melodic

Major Scales in 3rds ♩ = 80

C Major

* Flutists playing an instrument with a B foot may play the low B instead of E.

G Major

F Major

Chromatic Scale ♩ = 80

Beginning on G

Pentatonic (Major) Scale ♩ = 80

Beginning on G

Arpeggios ♩ = 60

B Major

G♯ Minor

F♯ Major (enharmonic equivalent of G♭ Minor)

D♯ Minor (enharmonic equivalent of E♭ Minor)

D♭ Major (enharmonic equivalent of C♯ Minor)

B♭ Minor

Dominant 7th Arpeggios ♩ = 80

F Major

B♭ Major

Level 7

Overview

Scales	Keys	Range	Tempo	Note Values	Articulations
Major	all keys	2 octaves	♩ = 60	♫	See p. 4 for required articulations. Additional articulations for this level: 
Minor (harmonic and melodic)	all keys				
Major in 3rds	D, A, E♭				
Chromatic	Beginning on any note				
Whole-Tone	Beginning on C, F				
Arpeggios					
Major	all keys	2 octaves	♩ = 80	3 ♫	See p. 4 for required articulations.
Minor	all keys		♩ = 60	♫	See p. 4 for required articulations. Additional articulations for this level:
Dominant 7th of Major Keys	D, A, F♯	2 octaves	♩ = 60	♫	See p. 4 for required articulations. Additional articulations for this level:
Diminished 7th of Minor Keys	D				
Overlapping Arpeggios (Three-note Pattern)					
Major	C, G, F	2 octaves	♩ = 80	3 ♫	See p. 4 for required articulations.
Minor	A, E, D				

* Two-octave exercises beginning on B must be played up to B3.

Scales ♩ = 60

C Major

C Minor Harmonic

C Minor Melodic

Db Major (enharmonic equivalent of C# Major)

C# Minor Harmonic

C# Minor Melodic

D Major

D Minor Harmonic

D Minor Melodic

Eb Major

D# Minor Harmonic (enharmonic equivalent of Eb Minor)

D# Minor Melodic (enharmonic equivalent of Eb Minor)

E Major

E Minor Harmonic

E Minor Melodic

F Major

F Minor Harmonic

F Minor Melodic

F# Major (enharmonic equivalent of G♭ Minor)

F# Minor Harmonic

F# Minor Melodic

G Major

G Minor Harmonic

G Minor Melodic

A♭ Major

G♯ Minor Harmonic

G♯ Minor Melodic

A Major

A Minor Harmonic

A Minor Melodic

B♭ Major

B♭ Minor Harmonic

B♭ Minor Melodic

B Major

B Minor Harmonic

B Minor Melodic

Major Scales in 3rds ♩ = 60

D Major

A Major

Eb Major

Chromatic Scales ♩ = 60

Beginning on C

Beginning on C# (enharmonic equivalent of Db)

Beginning on any note
 – follow the pattern established in the above examples

Whole-Tone Scales ♩ = 60

Beginning on C

Beginning on F

Arpeggios

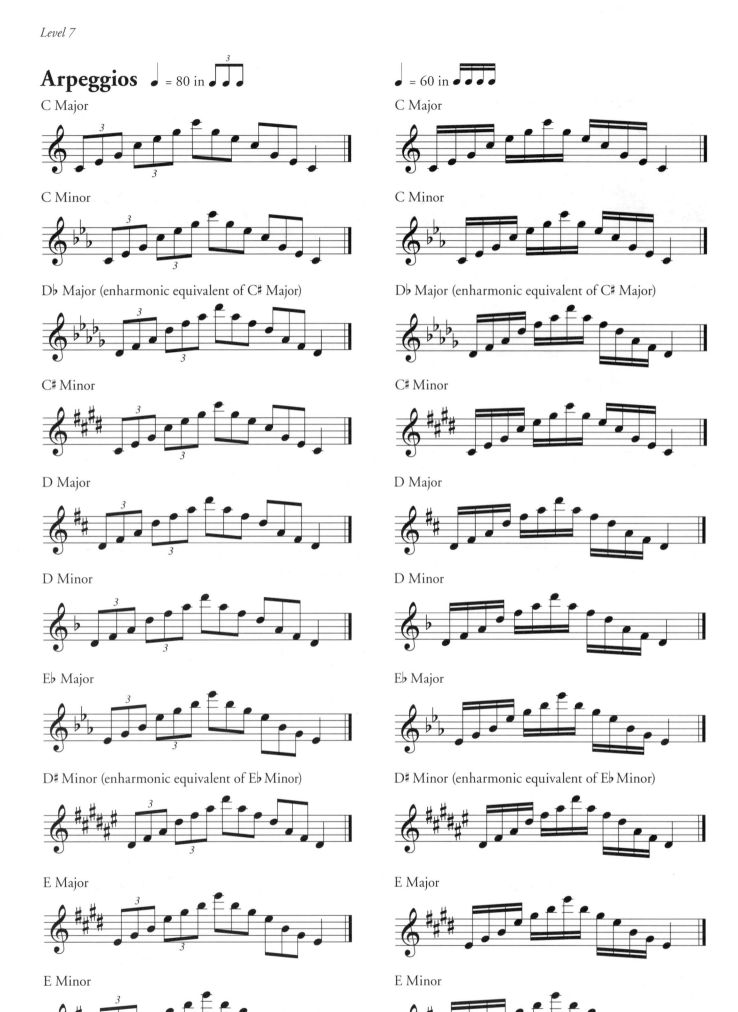

F Major

F Major

F Minor

F Minor

F# Major (enharmonic equivalent of G♭ Major)

F# Major (enharmonic equivalent of G♭ Major)

F# Minor

F# Minor

G Major

G Major

G Minor

G Minor

A♭ Major

A♭ Major

G# Minor

G# Minor

A Major

A Major

A Minor

A Minor

B♭ Major

B♭ Major

B♭ Minor

B♭ Minor

B Major

B Major

B Minor

B Minor

Dominant 7th Arpeggios ♩ = 60

D Major

F♯ Major (enharmonic equivalent of G♭ Major)

A Major

Diminished 7th Arpeggio  = 60

D Minor

Overlapping Arpeggios (Three-note Pattern) = 80

C Major

A Minor

G Major

E Minor

F Major

D Minor

Level 8

Overview

Scales	Keys	Range	Tempo	Note Values	Articulations
Major	all keys				See p. 4 for required articulations.
Minor (harmonic and melodic)	all keys	2 octaves	♩ = 60	♪♪♪♪	
Major in 3rds	E, A♭, D♭				
Chromatic	Beginning on any note				
Whole-Tone	Beginning on C♯, F♯				
Arpeggios					
Major	all keys	2 octaves	♩ = 80	³ ♪♪♪	See p. 4 for required articulations.
Minor	all keys		♩ = 60	♪♪♪♪	
Dominant 7th of Major Keys	B , E♭ , A♭	2 octaves	♩ = 60	♪♪♪♪	See p. 4 for required articulations.
Diminished 7th of Minor Keys	D, G				
Overlapping Arpeggios (Three-note Pattern)					
Major	all keys	2 octaves	♩ = 80	³ ♪♪♪	See p. 4 for required articulations.
Minor	all keys				

* Two-octave exercises beginning on B must be played up to B3.

Scales ♩ = 60

All major and minor keys
– see Level 7 for examples (p. 24)

Major Scales in 3rds ♩ = 60

E Major

A♭ Major

D♭ (enharmonic equivalent of D♯ Major)

Chromatic Scales ♩ = 60

Beginning on any note
– see Level 7 for examples (p. 29)

Whole-Tone Scales ♩ = 60

Beginning on C♯ (enharmonic equivalent of D♭)

Beginning on F♯ (enharmonic equivalent of G♭)

Arpeggios ♩ = 80 in ♪♪♪ ³   ♩ = 60 in ♬♬

All major and minor keys
– see Level 7 for examples (p. 30)

Dominant 7th Arpeggios ♩ = 60

B Major

E♭ Major

Ab Major

Diminished 7th Arpeggios   ♩ = 60

D Minor

G Minor

Overlapping Arpeggios (Three-note Pattern)   ♩ = 80

All major and minor keys
– see Level 7 for examples (p. 33)

Level 9

Overview

Scales	Keys	Range	Tempo	Note Values	Articulations
Major	all keys	2 octaves			See p. 4 for required articulations.
	C	3 octaves			
Minor (harmonic and melodic)	all keys	2 octaves			Additional articulation for this level:
	C	3 octaves	♩ = 80	♫♫	
Major in 3rds	all keys	2 octaves			
Chromatic	Beginning on C	3 octaves			
Whole-Tone	Beginning on C				
Arpeggios					
Major	all keys	2 octaves			See p. 4 for required articulations.
	C	3 octaves	♩ = 80	♫♫	
Minor	all keys	2 octaves			Additional articulation for this level:
	C	3 octaves			
Dominant 7th of Major Keys	all keys	2 octaves			
	F	3 octaves	♩ = 80	♫♫	
Diminished 7th of Minor Keys	all keys	2 octaves			
	C♯	3 octaves			
Overlapping Arpeggios (Four-note Pattern)					
Major	all keys				See p. 4 for required articulations.
Minor	all keys				Additional articulation for this level:
Dominant 7th of Major keys	C, G, F	2 octaves	♩ = 80	♫♫	
Diminished 7th of Minor keys	A, D, G				

* Two-octave exercises beginning on B must be played up to B3.

Scales ♩ = 80

All major and minor keys (2 octaves)
– see Level 7 for examples (p. 24)

C Major (3 octaves)

C Minor Harmonic (3 octaves)

C Minor Melodic (3 octaves)

Major Scales in 3rds ♩ = 80

All major keys (2 octaves)
– see Levels 6, 7, and 8 for examples (pp. 22, 28, and 34)

F♯ Major (enharmonic equivalent of G♭ Major)

B♭ Major

B Major

Chromatic Scale ♩ = 80

Beginning on C (3 octaves)

Whole-Tone Scale ♩ = 80

Beginning on C (3 octaves)

Arpeggios ♩ = 80

All major and minor keys (2 octaves)
– see Level 7 for examples (p. 30)

C Major (3 octaves)

C Minor (3 octaves)

Dominant 7th Arpeggios ♩ = 80

C Major

G Major

D Major

A Major

E Major

B Major

F♯ Major (enharmonic equivalent of G♭ Major)

F Major

B♭ Major

E♭ Major

A♭ Major

D♭ Major (enharmonic equivalent of C♯ Major)

F Major (3 octaves)

Diminished 7th Arpeggios ♩ = 80

D Minor

A Minor

G Minor

Of all minor keys (2 octaves)
– follow the pattern established in the above examples

C♯ Minor (3 octaves)

Overlapping Arpeggios (Four-note Pattern) ♩ = 80

All major and minor keys
– follow the pattern established in the example below

C Major (2 octaves)

Dominant 7th Overlapping Arpeggios (Four-note Pattern) ♩ = 80

C Major

G Major

F Major

Diminished 7th Overlapping Arpeggios (Four-note Pattern) ♩ = 80

A Minor

D Minor

G Minor

Level 10

Overview

Scales	Keys	Range	Tempo	Note Values	Articulations
Major	all keys	2 octaves			See p. 4 for required articulations.
	B, C, C♯, D	3 octaves*			
Minor (harmonic and melodic)	all keys	2 octaves	♩ = 92	♪♪♪♪	
	B, C, C♯, D	3 octaves*			
Major in 3rds	all keys	2 octaves			
Chromatic	Beginning on C, C♯, D	3 octaves			
Whole-Tone	Beginning on C, C♯, D	3 octaves			
Arpeggios					
Major	all keys	2 octaves			See p. 4 for required articulations.
	B, C, C♯, D	3 octaves*			
Minor	all keys	2 octaves	♩ = 92	♪♪♪♪	
	B, C, C♯, D	3 octaves*			
Dominant 7th of Major Keys	all keys	2 octaves			
	F	3 octaves			
Diminished 7th of Minor Keys	all keys	2 octaves			
	C♯	3 octaves			
Overlapping Arpeggios (Four-note Pattern)					
Major	all keys				See p. 4 for required articulations.
Minor	all keys	2 octaves	♩ = 92	♬♬	
Dominant 7th of Major Keys	all keys				
Diminished 7th of Minor Keys	all keys				

*Two-octave exercises beginning on B must be played up to B3. Flutists playing an instrument with a C foot may omit the three-octave exercises beginning on B.

Scales ♩ = 92

All major and minor keys (2 octaves)
– see Level 7 for examples (p. 24)

B Major (3 octaves)

B Minor Harmonic (3 octaves)

B Minor Melodic (3 octaves)

C Major (3 octaves)

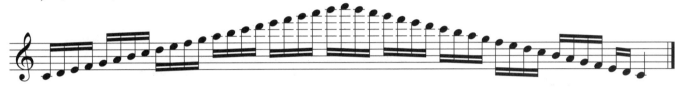

C Minor Harmonic (3 octaves)

C Minor Melodic (3 octaves)

C# Major (enharmonic eqivalent of D♭ Major) (3 octaves)

C# Minor Harmonic (3 octaves)

C# Minor Melodic (3 octaves)

D Major (3 octaves)

D Minor Harmonic (3 octaves)

D Minor Melodic (3 octaves)

Major Scales in 3rds ♩ = 92

All major keys
– see Level 9 for examples (p. 38)

Chromatic Scales ♩ = 92

Beginning on C
– see Level 9 (p. 39)

Beginning on C♯ (enharmonic eqivalent of D♭)

Beginning on D

Whole-Tone Scales ♩ = 92

Beginning on C

Beginning on C♯ (D♭)

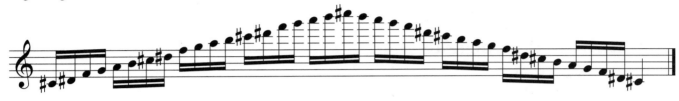

Beginning on D

Arpeggios ♩ = 92

All major and minor keys (2 octaves)
– see Level 7 for examples (p. 30)

B Major (3 octaves)

B Minor (3 octaves)

C Major (3 octaves)

C Minor (3 octaves)

C♯ Major (enharmonic eqivalent of D♭ Major) (3 octaves)

C♯ Minor (3 octaves)

D Major (3 octaves)

D Minor (3 octaves)

Dominant 7th Arpeggios ♩ = 92

Of all major keys (2 octaves)
– see Level 9 for examples (p. 39)

F Major (3 octaves)

Diminished 7th Arpeggios ♩ = 92

Of all minor keys (2 octaves)
– see Level 9 for examples (p. 40)

C♯ Minor (3 octaves)

Overlapping Arpeggios (Four-note Pattern) ♩ = 92

All major and minor keys (2 octaves)
– follow the pattern established in the example below

C Major

Dominant 7th Overlapping Arpeggios (Four-note Pattern) ♩ = 60

F Major

F♯ Major (enharmonic eqivalent of G♭ Major)

G Major

Ab Major

A Major

Bb Major

B Major

C Major

C# Major (enharmonic eqivalent of Db Major)

D Major

Eb Major

E Major

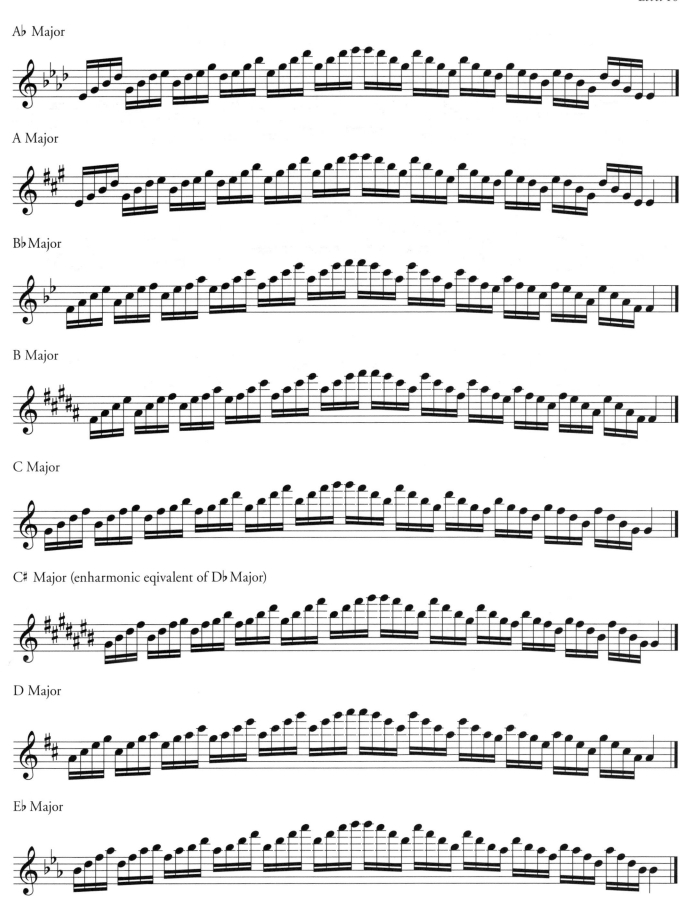

Diminished 7th Overlapping Arpeggios (Four-note Pattern) ♩ = 92

D Minor

A Minor

G Minor

Of all minor keys
– follow the pattern established in the above examples